This book belongs to

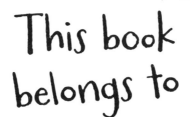

....

make
believe
ideas

The Ugly Duckling

Key sound short u spellings:
o, oe, ou, u

Secondary sounds: ck, sw, wh

Written by Rosie Greening
Illustrated by Clare Fennell

Reading with phonics

How to use this book

The **Reading with phonics** series helps you to have fun with your child and to support their learning of phonics and reading. It is aimed at children who have learned the letter sounds and are building confidence in their reading.

Each title in the series focuses on a different key sound or blend of sounds. The entertaining retelling of the story repeats this sound frequently, and the different spellings for the sound or blend of sounds are highlighted in red type. The first activity at the back of the book provides practice in reading and using words containing this sound or blend of sounds. The key sound for **The Ugly Duckling** is short u.

Start by reading the story to your child, asking them to join in with the refrain in bold. Next, encourage them to read the story with you. Give them a hand to decode tricky words.

Now look at the activity pages at the back of the book. These are intended for you and your child to enjoy together. Most are not activities to complete in pencil or pen, but by reading and talking or pointing.

The **Key sound** pages focus on one sound, and on the various different groups of letters that produce that sound. Encourage your child to read the different letter groups and complete the activity, so they become more aware of the variety of spellings there are for the same sound.

The **Letters together** pages look at three pairs or groups of letters and at the sounds they make as they work together. Help your child to read the words and trace the route on the word maps.

Rhyme is used a lot in these retellings. Whatever stage your child has reached in their learning of phonics, it is always good practice for them to listen carefully for sounds and find words that rhyme. The pages on **Rhyming words** take six words from the story and ask children to read and find other words that rhyme with them.

The **Key words** pages focus on a number of key words that occur regularly but can nonetheless be challenging. Many of these words are not sounded out following the rules of phonics and the easiest thing is for children to learn them by sight, so that they do not worry about decoding them. These pages encourage children to retell the story, practising key words as they do so.

The **Picture dictionary** page asks children to focus closely on nine words from the story. Encourage children to look carefully at each word, cover it with their hand, write it on a separate piece of paper, and finally, check it!

Do not complete all the activities at once – doing one each time you read will ensure that your child continues to enjoy the stories and the time you are spending together. **Have fun!**

There was a mother duck called May,
whose eggs began to crack one day.
"It's hatch o-clock!" she quacked with glee,
and so her friends rushed up to see.

The nest soon filled up with a crowd
of yellow ducklings, quacking loud.
Their mother proudly watched them hatch,
then spotted one that didn't match!

One is nothing like the rest,
and runs out of the comfy nest.

He wasn't yellow, cute and small –
this duckling looked all grey and tall!
The ducklings said, "He's not like us!"
and named their brother Ugly Gus.

Gus is nothing like the others.
He's much bigger than his brothers!

Poor Gus grew bigger by the day,
which made it tough for him to play.
The others weaved between the reeds,
while Gus got tangled in the weeds.
8

The yellow ducklings weren't polite
and talked about Gus every night.
"I wonder why he's big and grey?
He doesn't look like us!" they'd say.

Gus is nothing like the rest.
The other ducks think they're the best!

"If I were yellow too," Gus said,
"they might be nice to me instead."
He covered all his greyness up
with lovely yellow buttercups.

But when the buds made poor Gus sneeze,
the yellow ducklings laughed and teased.
So Gus rushed off to try his luck
and hunt for other ugly ducks.

Gus is nothing like the ducks.
He's feeling down and out of luck!

Young Gus had just begun to swim
when lots of grey birds honked at him.
He said, "Hello! I'm grey, like you.
Are you all ugly ducklings, too?"

Gus is nothing like the rest.
He's going on a duckling quest.

The birds honked angrily at Gus.
"We're geese!" they cried. "You're not like us!"
So Ugly Gus plunged back upstream
to find himself another team.

Gus is nothing like the rest.
The geese think he is just a pest.

Just then, some others fluttered by.

Gus shouted out, "I also fly!

You must be ugly ducks, like me!"

"We're gulls," they squawked. "Can you not see?"

SQUAWK!
SQUAWK!

Gus is nothing like the rest.
The flying gulls are not impressed.

17

Gus thought all the birds had flown.
He hated being on his own!
But in a flash of dazzling white,
some graceful birds sailed into sight.

They had long necks and orange beaks.
Young Gus was much too stunned to speak!
But suddenly, they called to Gus:
"Hello, there – will you swim with us?"

Gus is nothing like the rest.
They say to Gus, "Please be our guest!"

Said Gus, "That's what I'd love to do.
I only wish I looked like you!"
They laughed and said, "You are like us.
Just look at your reflection, Gus!"

Young Gus was dazed by what he saw –
he didn't look grey anymore!
His feathers were a lovely white.
The birds said, "You're a swan, alright!"

Gus is nothing like the rest.
His brothers never would have guessed!

Gus felt lucky as can be,
and started singing cheerfully:
"I won't feel ugly from now on.
I'm Gorgeous Gus, the stunning swan!"

Gus is nothing like the rest.
But being different is the best!

23

Key sound

There are several different groups of letters that make the **short u** sound. Practise them by looking at the words in the eggs and using them to make sentences.
Can you use each word in a different sentence?

duck ugly
rush bud up
but luck

brother
nothing
others lovely
covered

doesn't
does

double

young   rough

trouble

Letters together

Look at these groups of letters and say the sounds they make.

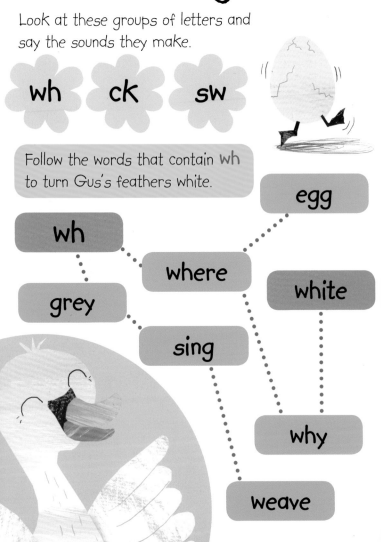

wh   **ck**   **sw**

Follow the words that contain wh to turn Gus's feathers white.

wh

grey

where

sing

egg

white

why

weave

Follow the words that contain ck to say goodbye to the ducks.

ck

clock

tough

luck

day

crack

big

ducks

back

Follow the words that contain sw to lead Gus to the swans.

swim

sack

sw

slip

find

swell

sweet

rush

swing

swans

27

Rhyming words

Read and say the words in the flowers and then point to other words that rhyme with them.

clock	luck
duck	
stuck	nest

night	nest
white	
reed	site

weird	treat
sweet	
team	feet

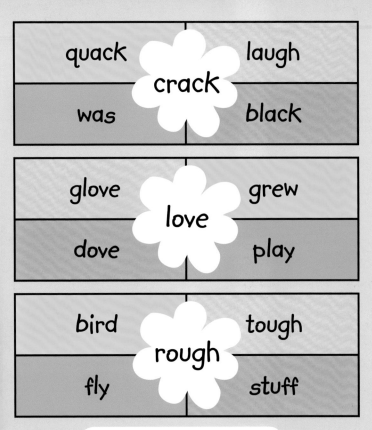

quack	**crack**	laugh
was		black

glove	**love**	grew
dove		play

bird	**rough**	tough
fly		stuff

Now choose a word and make up a rhyming chant!

The duck goes **quack** as her eggs **crack**!

29

Key words

Many common words can be tricky to sound out. Practise them by reading these sentences about the story. Now make more sentences using other key words from around the border.

Mother May **had** some eggs.

One egg **was** different to the rest.

The yellow ducklings **were** mean to Gus.

Gus ran **off** to find more birds like him.

not • your • asked • got • he

• said • were • a • big • had • made • day • off • we •

The geese didn't **look** like Gus.

Then Gus saw some graceful birds.

They had long necks and white feathers.

The **big** swans asked Gus to join them.

Gus realised **he** was a swan!

all · saw · and · then · house · the · called · look · my · about · up · you · they ·

old · there · like · into · of · with · was · dad

Picture dictionary

Look carefully at the pictures and the words.
Now cover the words, one at a time.
Can you remember how to write them?

buttercup

duck

duckling

egg

geese

gull

nest

reeds

swan